Name

Address

Telephone

Email

Club/School   Membership No.

Diving Qualifications

I0166875

Log Book No.

If you find this log book please contact the owner using the details above

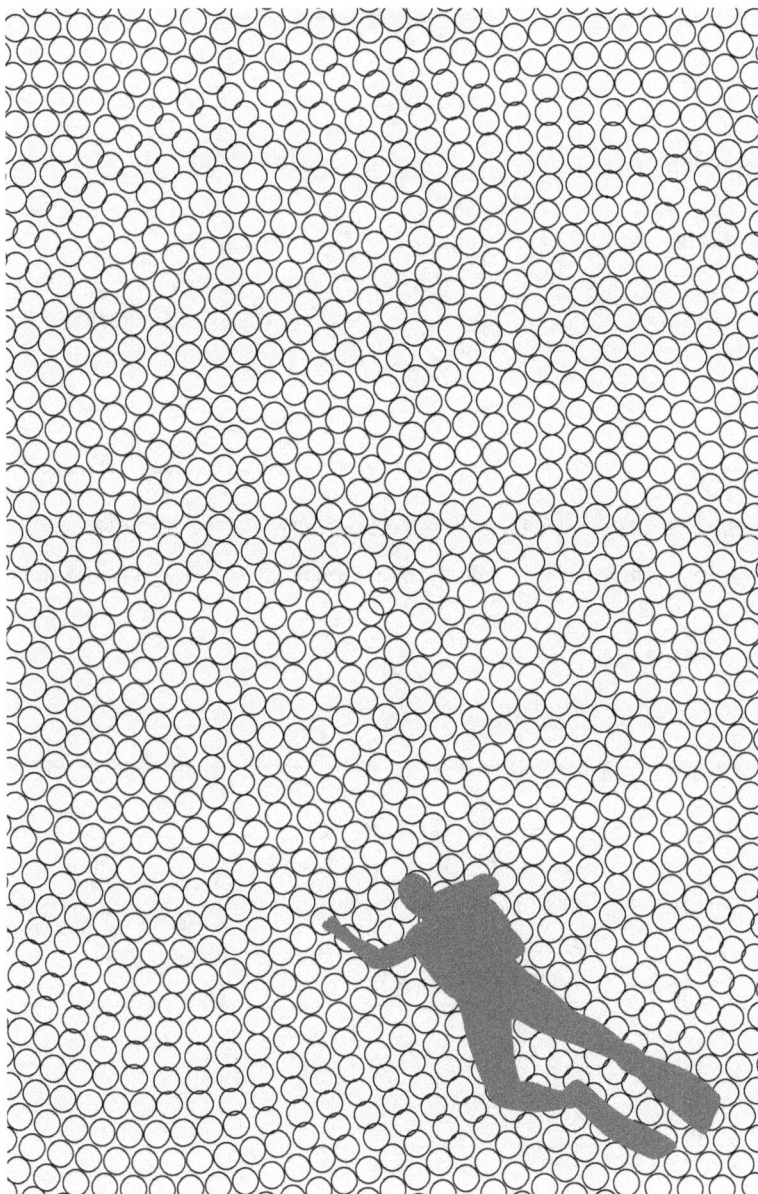

YOUR
DIVE LOGS

DIVE No.	DIVE LOG	Date

Dive Site Boat/Shore/Inland

Buddies

Boat/Skipper Port/Launch Site

Dive of Day 1 2 3 4 Surface Int. : Time in : out :

Mix	Pressure		Used	Cyl. Size	DIVE TIME	MAX DEPTH
	In	Out				
					mins	m/ft

Tissue Code: Pre Post Deco Stops......... mins .... m/ft ....mins........ m/ft

Equipment Notes	Weather/Sea Conditions	Training/Practice Needed

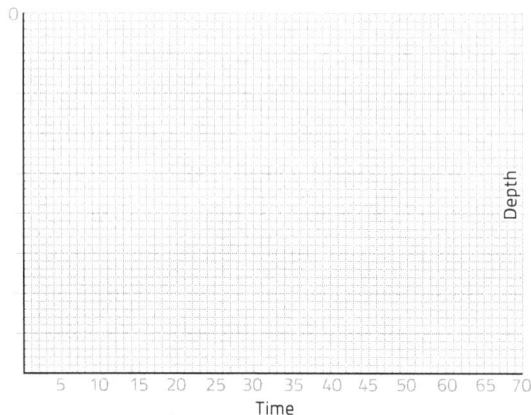

Issues

Nitrogen Narcosis

Buddy Separation

Kit Failure

Working Hard

Unhappy

Missed Deco Stop

Other

Depth

Time

5 10 15 20 25 30 35 40 45 50 55 60 65 70

Summary

Estimated Visibility

_______________ m/ft

Description/Sketch/Memory of Dive

Accumulated Dive Time

:

Milestone

Name

Signature

No.

Verified by

DIVE No.	DIVE LOG	Date

Dive Site Boat/Shore/Inland

Buddies

Boat/Skipper Port/Launch Site

Dive of Day 1 2 3 4   Surface Int.   :   Time in   :   out   :

Mix	Pressure		Used	Cyl. Size	DIVE TIME	MAX DEPTH
	In	Out				
					mins	m/ft

Tissue Code: Pre   Post   Deco Stops......... mins .... m/ft ....mins........ m/ft

Equipment Notes	Weather/Sea Conditions	Training/Practice Needed

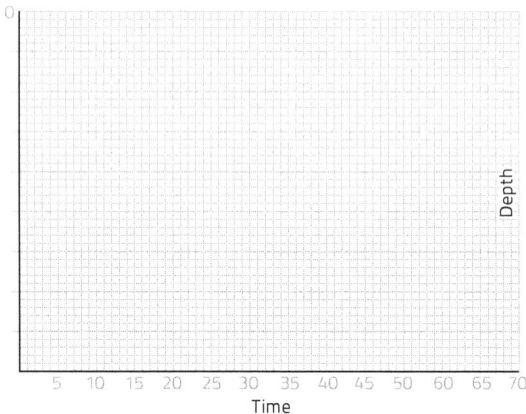

Depth

Time
5 10 15 20 25 30 35 40 45 50 55 60 65 70

Issues

Nitrogen Narcosis

Buddy Separation

Kit Failure

Working Hard

Unhappy

Missed Deco Stop

Other

Summary

Estimated Visibility

______ m/ft

Description/Sketch/Memory of Dive

Accumulated Dive Time

:

Milestone

Name

Signature

No.

Verified by

DIVE No.	DIVE LOG	Date

Dive Site   Boat/Shore/Inland

Buddies

Boat/Skipper   Port/Launch Site

Dive of Day   1   2   3   4   Surface Int.   :   Time in   :   out   :

	Pressure			Cyl.	DIVE TIME	MAX DEPTH
Mix	In	Out	Used	Size		
					mins	m/ft

Tissue Code: Pre   Post | Deco Stops......... mins .... m/ft ....mins........ m/ft

Equipment Notes	Weather/Sea Conditions	Training/Practice Needed

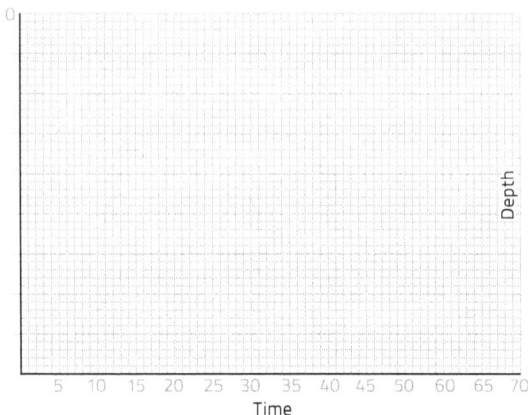

Time

Depth

Issues

Nitrogen Narcosis

Buddy Separation

Kit Failure

Working Hard

Unhappy

Missed Deco Stop

Other

Summary

Estimated Visibility

_____ m/ft

Description/Sketch/Memory of Dive

Accumulated Dive Time

:

Milestone

Name

Signature

No.

Verified by

DIVE No.	DIVE LOG	Date

Dive Site   Boat/Shore/Inland

Buddies

Boat/Skipper   Port/Launch Site

Dive of Day 1 2 3 4 | Surface Int.   : | Time in   :   out   :

Mix	Pressure In	Pressure Out	Used	Cyl. Size	DIVE TIME	MAX DEPTH
					mins	m/ft

Tissue Code: Pre   Post   Deco Stops......... mins .... m/ft ....mins........ m/ft

Equipment Notes	Weather/Sea Conditions	Training/Practice Needed

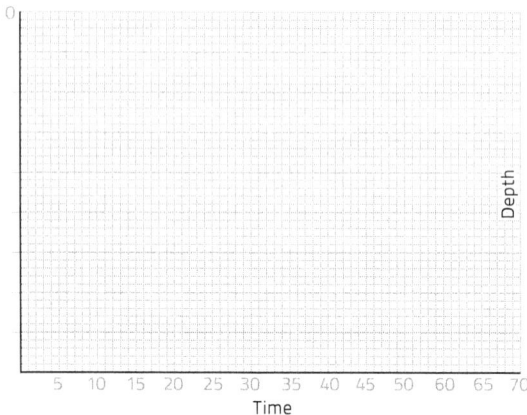

Time

Issues

Nitrogen Narcosis

Buddy Separation

Kit Failure

Working Hard

Unhappy

Missed Deco Stop

Other

Summary

Estimated Visibility

_____m/ft

Description/Sketch/Memory of Dive

Accumulated Dive Time

:

Milestone

Name

Signature

No.

Verified by

DIVE No.	DIVE LOG	Date

Dive Site   Boat/Shore/Inland

Buddies

Boat/Skipper   Port/Launch Site

Dive of Day   1   2   3   4   Surface Int.   :   Time in   :   out   :

Mix	Pressure In	Pressure Out	Used	Cyl. Size	DIVE TIME	MAX DEPTH
					mins	m/ft

Tissue Code: Pre   Post   Deco Stops......... mins .... m/ft ....mins........ m/ft

Equipment Notes	Weather/Sea Conditions	Training/Practice Needed

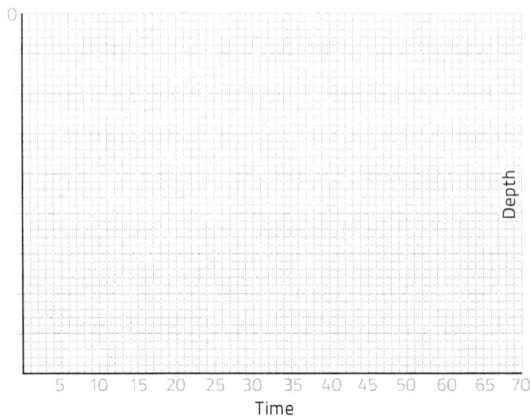

Time

Depth

Issues

Nitrogen Narcosis

Buddy Separation

Kit Failure

Working Hard

Unhappy

Missed Deco Stop

Other

Summary

Estimated Visibility

_____ m/ft

Description/Sketch/Memory of Dive

Accumulated Dive Time		
:	Name	**Verified by**
Milestone	Signature	
	No.	

DIVE No.	**DIVE LOG**	**Date**

Dive Site   Boat/Shore/Inland

Buddies

Boat/Skipper   Port/Launch Site

Dive of Day 1 2 3 4   Surface Int.   :   Time in   :   out   :

	Pressure			Cyl.	**DIVE TIME**	**MAX DEPTH**
Mix	In	Out	Used	Size		
					mins	m/ft

Tissue Code: Pre   Post   Deco Stops......... mins .... m/ft ....mins........ m/ft

Equipment Notes	Weather/Sea Conditions	Training/Practice Needed

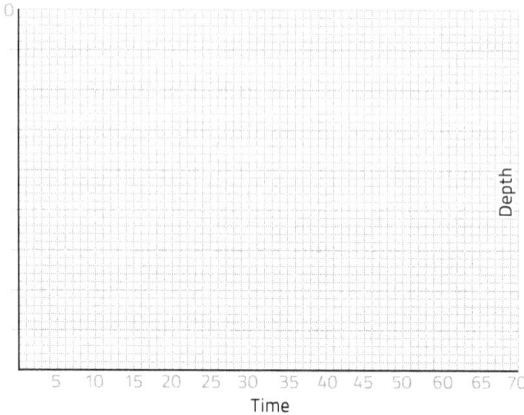

Depth / Time

Issues

Nitrogen Narcosis

Buddy Separation

Kit Failure

Working Hard

Unhappy

Missed Deco Stop

Other

Summary

Estimated Visibility

_____ m/ft

Description/Sketch/Memory of Dive

Accumulated Dive Time

:

Milestone

Name

Signature

No.

Verified by

DIVE No.	DIVE LOG	Date

Dive Site   Boat/Shore/Inland

Buddies

Boat/Skipper   Port/Launch Site

Dive of Day   1   2   3   4   Surface Int.   :   Time in   :   out   :

Mix	Pressure In	Out	Used	Cyl. Size	DIVE TIME	MAX DEPTH
					mins	m/ft

Tissue Code: Pre   Post   Deco Stops......... mins .... m/ft ....mins........ m/ft

Equipment Notes	Weather/Sea Conditions	Training/Practice Needed

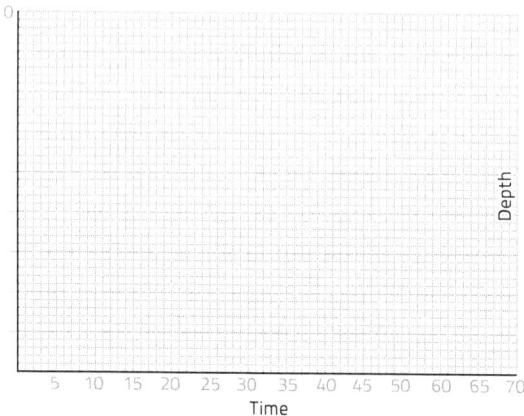

Depth / Time graph

5   10   15   20   25   30   35   40   45   50   55   60   65   70

Time

Issues

Nitrogen Narcosis

Buddy Separation

Kit Failure

Working Hard

Unhappy

Missed Deco Stop

Other

Summary

Estimated Visibility

_____ m/ft

Description/Sketch/Memory of Dive

Accumulated Dive Time

:

Milestone

Name

Signature

No.

Verified by

DIVE No.	DIVE LOG	Date

Dive Site Boat/Shore/Inland

Buddies

Boat/Skipper Port/Launch Site

Dive of Day 1 2 3 4 | Surface Int. : | Time in : out :

Mix	Pressure		Used	Cyl. Size	DIVE TIME	MAX DEPTH
	In	Out				
					mins	m/ft

Tissue Code: Pre   Post   Deco Stops......... mins........ m/ft ....mins........ m/ft

Equipment Notes	Weather/Sea Conditions	Training/Practice Needed

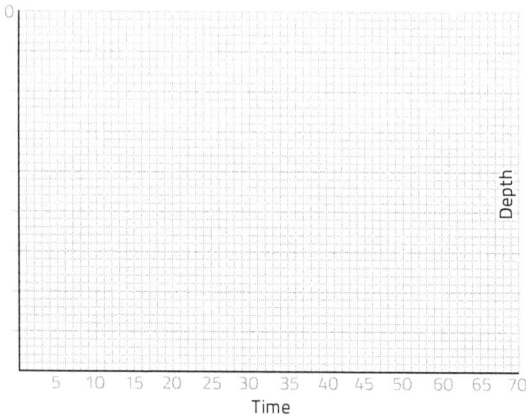

Issues

Nitrogen Narcosis

Buddy Separation

Kit Failure

Working Hard

Unhappy

Missed Deco Stop

Other

Depth

Time

5 10 15 20 25 30 35 40 45 50 55 60 65 70

Summary

Estimated Visibility

_____ m/ft

Description/Sketch/Memory of Dive

Accumulated Dive Time	Name	**Verified by**
:	Signature	
Milestone	No.	

DIVE No.	DIVE LOG	Date

Dive Site Boat/Shore/Inland

Buddies

Boat/Skipper Port/Launch Site

Dive of Day 1 2 3 4 Surface Int. : Time in : out :

Mix	Pressure		Used	Cyl. Size	DIVE TIME	MAX DEPTH
	In	Out				
					mins	m/ft

Tissue Code: Pre   Post   Deco Stops......... mins .... m/ft ....mins........ m/ft

Equipment Notes	Weather/Sea Conditions	Training/Practice Needed

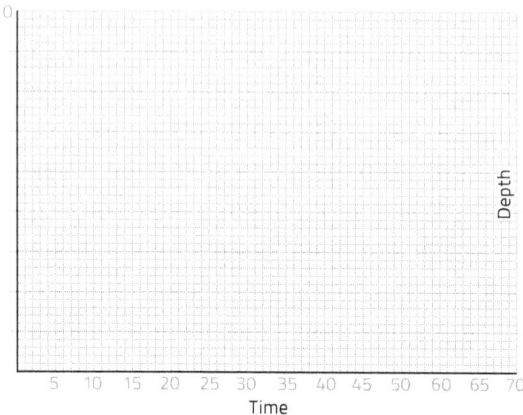

0

Depth

Time
5 10 15 20 25 30 35 40 45 50 60 65 70

Issues

Nitrogen Narcosis

Buddy Separation

Kit Failure

Working Hard

Unhappy

Missed Deco Stop

Other

Summary

Estimated Visibility

_____ m/ft

Description/Sketch/Memory of Dive

Accumulated Dive Time

:

Milestone

Name

Signature

No.

Verified by

DIVE No.	DIVE LOG	Date

Dive Site   Boat/Shore/Inland

Buddies

Boat/Skipper   Port/Launch Site

Dive of Day   1   2   3   4   Surface Int.   :   Time in   :   out   :

Mix	Pressure In	Out	Used	Cyl. Size	DIVE TIME	MAX DEPTH
					mins	m/ft

Tissue Code: Pre   Post   Deco Stops......... mins........ m/ft ....mins........ m/ft

Equipment Notes	Weather/Sea Conditions	Training/Practice Needed

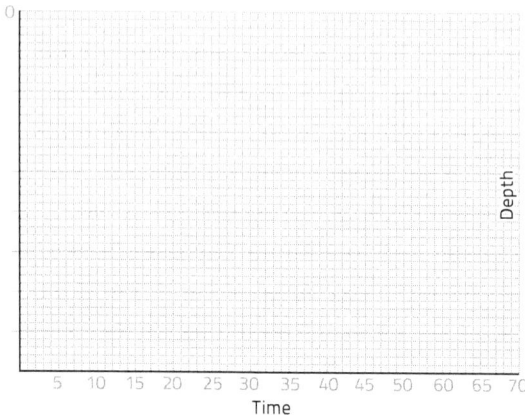

Time

Depth

Issues

Nitrogen Narcosis

Buddy Separation

Kit Failure

Working Hard

Unhappy

Missed Deco Stop

Other _____

Summary

Estimated Visibility

_____m/ft

Description/Sketch/Memory of Dive

Accumulated Dive Time

:

Milestone

Name

Signature

No.

Verified by

DIVE No.	DIVE LOG	Date

Dive Site Boat/Shore/Inland

Buddies

Boat/Skipper   Port/Launch Site

Dive of Day 1 2 3 4   Surface Int.   :   Time in   :   out   :

Mix	Pressure		Used	Cyl. Size	DIVE TIME	MAX DEPTH
	In	Out				
					mins	m/ft

Tissue Code: Pre   Post   Deco Stops......... mins........ m/ft ....mins........ m/ft

Equipment Notes	Weather/Sea Conditions	Training/Practice Needed

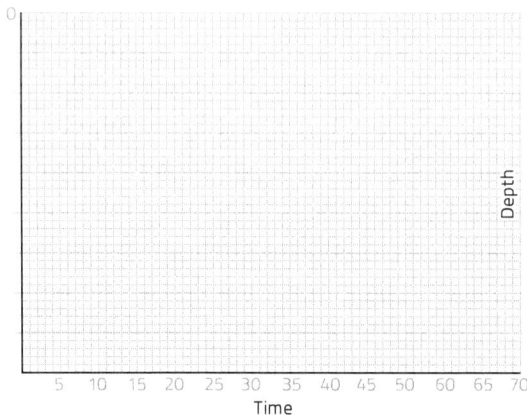

Issues

Nitrogen Narcosis

Buddy Separation

Kit Failure

Working Hard

Unhappy

Missed Deco Stop

Other

Depth

5   10   15   20   25   30   35   40   45   50   55   60   65   70
Time

Summary

Estimated Visibility

_____ m/ft

Description/Sketch/Memory of Dive

Accumulated Dive Time

:

Milestone

Name

Signature

No.

Verified by

DIVE No.	DIVE LOG	Date

Dive Site   Boat/Shore/Inland

Buddies

Boat/Skipper   Port/Launch Site

Dive of Day   1   2   3   4   Surface Int.   :   Time in   :   out   :

	Pressure			Cyl.	DIVE TIME	MAX DEPTH
Mix	In	Out	Used	Size		
					mins	m/ft

Tissue Code: Pre   Post   Deco Stops......... mins .... m/ft ....mins........ m/ft

Equipment Notes	Weather/Sea Conditions	Training/Practice Needed

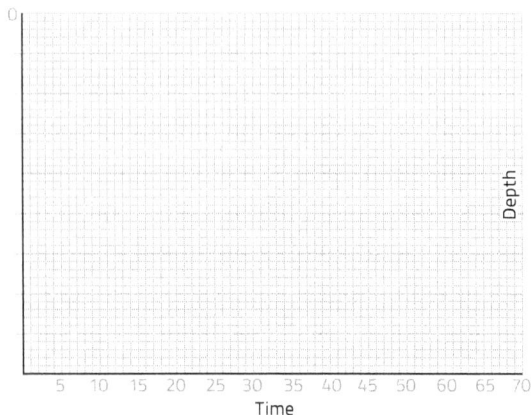

Issues

Nitrogen Narcosis

Buddy Separation

Kit Failure

Working Hard

Unhappy

Missed Deco Stop

Other

Depth

5   10   15   20   25   30   35   40   45   50   60   65   70

Time

Summary

Estimated Visibility

_____ m/ft

Description/Sketch/Memory of Dive

Accumulated Dive Time

:

Milestone

Name

Signature

No.

Verified by

DIVE No.	DIVE LOG	Date

Dive Site   Boat/Shore/Inland

Buddies

Boat/Skipper   Port/Launch Site

Dive of Day   1   2   3   4   Surface Int.   :   Time in   :   out   :

Mix	Pressure		Used	Cyl. Size	DIVE TIME	MAX DEPTH
	In	Out				
					mins	m/ft

Tissue Code: Pre   Post   Deco Stops......... mins .... m/ft ....mins........ m/ft

Equipment Notes	Weather/Sea Conditions	Training/Practice Needed

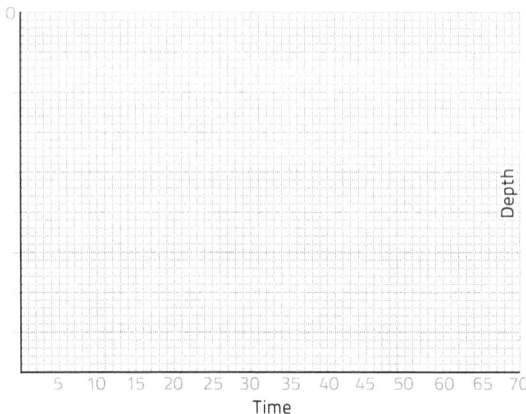

Issues

Nitrogen Narcosis

Buddy Separation

Kit Failure

Working Hard

Unhappy

Missed Deco Stop

Other _____

_____

Depth

5   10   15   20   25   30   35   40   45   50   60   65   70

Time

Summary

Estimated Visibility

_____m/ft

Description/Sketch/Memory of Dive

Accumulated Dive Time

:

Milestone

Name

Signature

No.

Verified by

DIVE No.	DIVE LOG	Date

Dive Site Boat/Shore/Inland

Buddies

Boat/Skipper Port/Launch Site

Dive of Day 1 2 3 4 | Surface Int. : | Time in : out :

Mix	Pressure		Used	Cyl. Size	DIVE TIME	MAX DEPTH
	In	Out				
					mins	m/ft

Tissue Code: Pre Post | Deco Stops......... mins .... m/ft ....mins........ m/ft

Equipment Notes	Weather/Sea Conditions	Training/Practice Needed

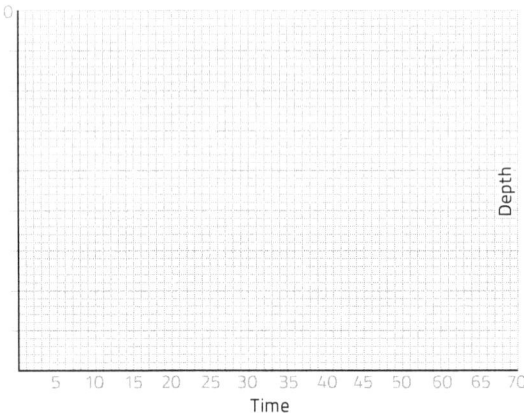

0

Depth

5 10 15 20 25 30 35 40 45 50 60 65 70
Time

Issues

Nitrogen Narcosis

Buddy Separation

Kit Failure

Working Hard

Unhappy

Missed Deco Stop

Other

Summary

Summary

Estimated Visibility

_____ m/ft

Description/Sketch/Memory of Dive

Accumulated Dive Time	Name	Verified by
:	Signature	
Milestone	No.	

| DIVE No. | DIVE LOG | Date |

Dive Site Boat/Shore/Inland

Buddies

Boat/Skipper Port/Launch Site

Dive of Day 1 2 3 4 | Surface Int. : | Time in : out :

Mix	Pressure In	Out	Used	Cyl. Size	**DIVE TIME**	**MAX DEPTH**
					mins	m/ft

Tissue Code: Pre Post | Deco Stops......... mins .... m/ft ....mins........ m/ft

Equipment Notes	Weather/Sea Conditions	Training/Practice Needed

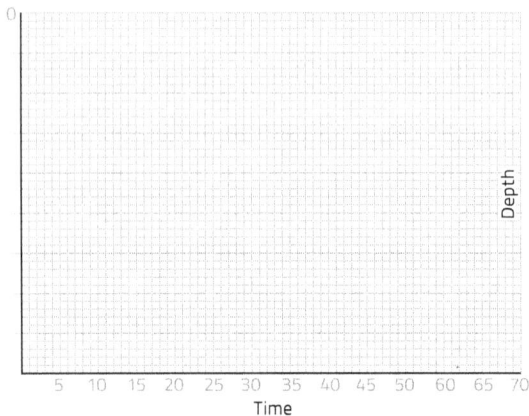

Issues

Nitrogen Narcosis

Buddy Separation

Kit Failure

Working Hard

Unhappy

Missed Deco Stop

Other

Depth

Time

5 10 15 20 25 30 35 40 45 50 60 65 70

Summary

Estimated Visibility

_____ m/ft

Description/Sketch/Memory of Dive

Accumulated Dive Time

:

Milestone

Name

Signature

No.

Verified by

DIVE No.	DIVE LOG	Date

Dive Site   Boat/Shore/Inland

Buddies

Boat/Skipper   Port/Launch Site

Dive of Day   1   2   3   4   Surface Int.   :   Time in   :   out   :

Mix	Pressure In	Out	Used	Cyl. Size	DIVE TIME	MAX DEPTH
					mins	m/ft

Tissue Code: Pre   Post   Deco Stops......... mins........ m/ft ....mins........ m/ft

Equipment Notes	Weather/Sea Conditions	Training/Practice Needed

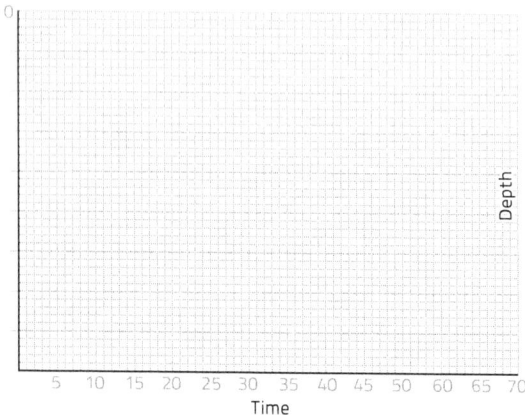

0

Depth

Issues

Nitrogen Narcosis

Buddy Separation

Kit Failure

Working Hard

Unhappy

Missed Deco Stop

Other _____

5   10   15   20   25   30   35   40   45   50   60   65   70

Time

Summary

Description/Sketch/Memory of Dive

Accumulated Dive Time	Name	**Verified by**
:	Signature	
Milestone	No.	

DIVE No.	DIVE LOG	Date

Dive Site   Boat/Shore/Inland

Buddies

Boat/Skipper   Port/Launch Site

Dive of Day 1 2 3 4   Surface Int.   :   Time in   :   out   :

Mix	Pressure		Used	Cyl. Size	DIVE TIME	MAX DEPTH
	In	Out				
					mins	m/ft

Tissue Code: Pre   Post   Deco Stops......... mins........ m/ft ....mins........ m/ft

Equipment Notes	Weather/Sea Conditions	Training/Practice Needed

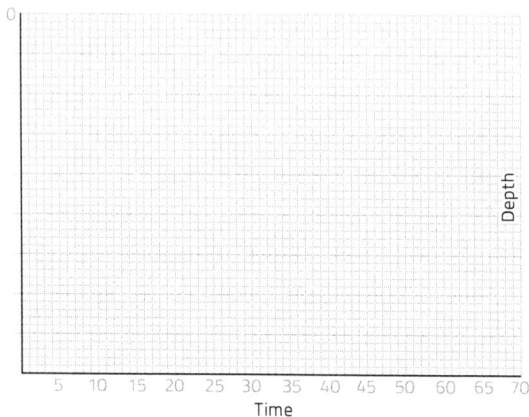

Issues

Nitrogen Narcosis

Buddy Separation

Kit Failure

Working Hard

Unhappy

Missed Deco Stop

Other

Depth

Time

5 10 15 20 25 30 35 40 45 50 55 60 65 70

Summary

Description/Sketch/Memory of Dive

Accumulated Dive Time

:

Milestone

Name

Signature

No.

Verified by

DIVE No.	DIVE LOG	Date

Dive Site   Boat/Shore/Inland

Buddies

Boat/Skipper   Port/Launch Site

Dive of Day 1 2 3 4   Surface Int.   :   Time in   :   out   :

| | Pressure | | | Cyl. | **DIVE TIME** | **MAX DEPTH** |
Mix	In	Out	Used	Size		
					mins	m/ft

Tissue Code: Pre   Post   Deco Stops......... mins .... m/ft ....mins........ m/ft

Equipment Notes	Weather/Sea Conditions	Training/Practice Needed

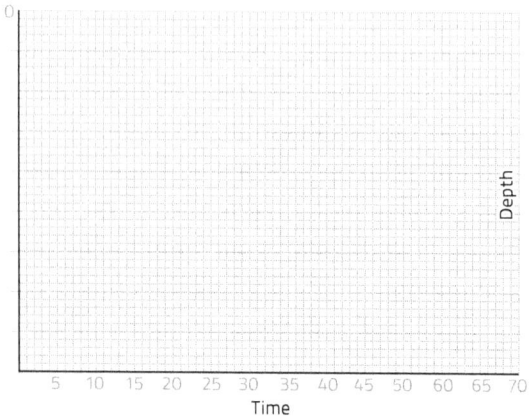

Time

Depth

Issues

Nitrogen Narcosis

Buddy Separation

Kit Failure

Working Hard

Unhappy

Missed Deco Stop

Other

Summary

Estimated Visibility

____________ m/ft

Description/Sketch/Memory of Dive

Accumulated Dive Time

:

Milestone

Name

Signature

No.

Verified by

DIVE No.	DIVE LOG	Date

Dive Site   Boat/Shore/Inland

Buddies

Boat/Skipper   Port/Launch Site

Dive of Day 1 2 3 4	Surface Int. :	Time in : out :

Mix	Pressure In	Pressure Out	Used	Cyl. Size	DIVE TIME	MAX DEPTH
					mins	m/ft

Tissue Code: Pre   Post   Deco Stops......... mins .... m/ft ....mins........ m/ft

Equipment Notes	Weather/Sea Conditions	Training/Practice Needed

Issues

Nitrogen Narcosis

Buddy Separation

Kit Failure

Working Hard

Unhappy

Missed Deco Stop

Other

Summary

Estimated Visibility
_____m/ft

Description/Sketch/Memory of Dive

Accumulated Dive Time

:

Milestone

Name

Signature

No.

Verified by

DIVE No.	DIVE LOG	Date

Dive Site Boat/Shore/Inland

Buddies

Boat/Skipper Port/Launch Site

Dive of Day 1 2 3 4 | Surface Int. : | Time in : out :

Mix	Pressure		Used	Cyl. Size	DIVE TIME	MAX DEPTH
	In	Out				
					mins	m/ft

Tissue Code: Pre Post | Deco Stops......... mins........ m/ft ....mins........ m/ft

Equipment Notes	Weather/Sea Conditions	Training/Practice Needed

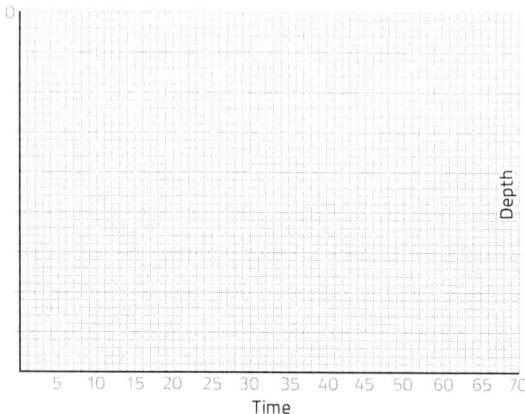

Depth

Time
5 10 15 20 25 30 35 40 45 50 55 60 65 70

Issues

Nitrogen Narcosis

Buddy Separation

Kit Failure

Working Hard

Unhappy

Missed Deco Stop

Other

Summary

Estimated Visibility

______ m/ft

Description/Sketch/Memory of Dive

Accumulated Dive Time

:

Milestone

Name

Verified by

Signature

No.

DIVE No.	DIVE LOG	Date

Dive Site   Boat/Shore/Inland

Buddies

Boat/Skipper   Port/Launch Site

Dive of Day   1   2   3   4   Surface Int.   :   Time in   :   out   :

	Pressure			Cyl.	DIVE TIME	MAX DEPTH
Mix	In	Out	Used	Size		
					mins	m/ft

Tissue Code: Pre   Post   Deco Stops......... mins .... m/ft ....mins........ m/ft

Equipment Notes	Weather/Sea Conditions	Training/Practice Needed

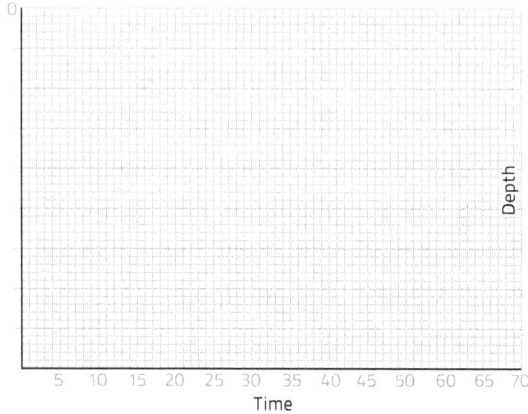

Issues

Nitrogen Narcosis

Buddy Separation

Kit Failure

Working Hard

Unhappy

Missed Deco Stop

Other

Depth

5   10   15   20   25   30   35   40   45   50   60   65   70

Time

Summary

Estimated Visibility

_____ m/ft

Description/Sketch/Memory of Dive

Accumulated Dive Time	Name	**Verified by**
:	Signature	
Milestone	No.	

DIVE No.	DIVE LOG	Date

Dive Site   Boat/Shore/Inland

Buddies

Boat/Skipper   Port/Launch Site

Dive of Day 1 2 3 4   Surface Int. :   Time in :   out :

Mix	Pressure		Used	Cyl. Size	DIVE TIME	MAX DEPTH
	In	Out				
					mins	m/ft

Tissue Code: Pre   Post   Deco Stops......... mins........ m/ft ....mins........ m/ft

Equipment Notes	Weather/Sea Conditions	Training/Practice Needed

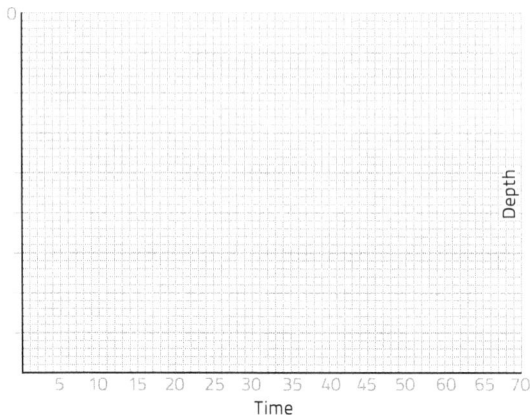
Depth / Time

Issues

Nitrogen Narcosis

Buddy Separation

Kit Failure

Working Hard

Unhappy

Missed Deco Stop

Other

Summary

Estimated Visibility

_____ m/ft

Description/Sketch/Memory of Dive

Accumulated Dive Time	Name	**Verified by**
:	Signature	
Milestone	No.	

DIVE No.	DIVE LOG	Date

Dive Site   Boat/Shore/Inland

Buddies

Boat/Skipper   Port/Launch Site

Dive of Day 1 2 3 4 | Surface Int.   : | Time in   :   out   :

Mix	Pressure		Used	Cyl. Size	DIVE TIME	MAX DEPTH
	In	Out				
					mins	m/ft

Tissue Code: Pre   Post   Deco Stops......... mins........ m/ft ....mins........ m/ft

Equipment Notes	Weather/Sea Conditions	Training/Practice Needed

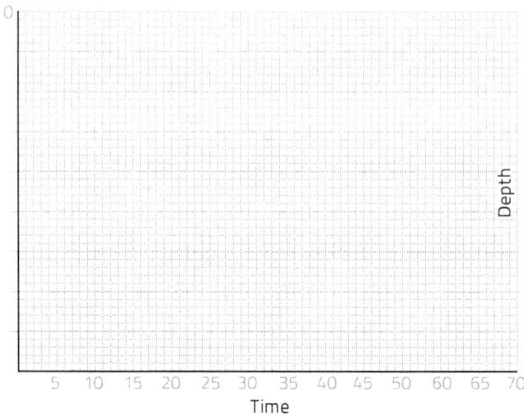

Issues

Nitrogen Narcosis

Buddy Separation

Kit Failure

Working Hard

Unhappy

Missed Deco Stop

Other

Depth

5 10 15 20 25 30 35 40 45 50 55 60 65 70

Time

Summary

Description/Sketch/Memory of Dive

Accumulated Dive Time	Name	**Verified by**
:	Signature	
Milestone	No.	

DIVE No.	DIVE LOG	Date

Dive Site Boat/Shore/Inland

Buddies

Boat/Skipper Port/Launch Site

Dive of Day 1 2 3 4 | Surface Int. : | Time in : out :

	Pressure			Cyl.	**DIVE TIME**	**MAX DEPTH**
Mix	In	Out	Used	Size		
					mins	m/ft

Tissue Code: Pre   Post   Deco Stops......... mins .... m/ft ....mins........ m/ft

Equipment Notes	Weather/Sea Conditions	Training/Practice Needed

Issues

Nitrogen Narcosis

Buddy Separation

Kit Failure

Working Hard

Unhappy

Missed Deco Stop

Other

Depth

Time

5 10 15 20 25 30 35 40 45 50 60 65 70

Summary

Estimated Visibility

_____ m/ft

Description/Sketch/Memory of Dive

Accumulated Dive Time

:

Milestone

Name

Signature

No.

Verified by

DIVE No.	DIVE LOG	Date

Dive Site Boat/Shore/Inland

Buddies

Boat/Skipper Port/Launch Site

Dive of Day 1 2 3 4   Surface Int. :   Time in :   out :

	Pressure			Cyl.	**DIVE TIME**	**MAX DEPTH**
Mix	In	Out	Used	Size		
					mins	m/ft

Tissue Code: Pre   Post   Deco Stops......... mins........ m/ft ....mins........ m/ft

Equipment Notes	Weather/Sea Conditions	Training/Practice Needed

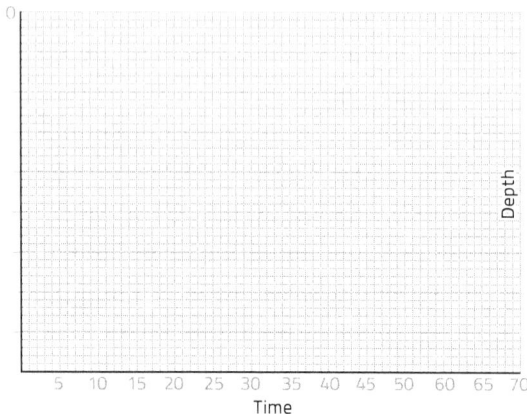

0

Depth

Time
5 10 15 20 25 30 35 40 45 50 60 65 70

Issues

Nitrogen Narcosis

Buddy Separation

Kit Failure

Working Hard

Unhappy

Missed Deco Stop

Other _____

Summary

Estimated Visibility

__________ m/ft

Description/Sketch/Memory of Dive

Accumulated Dive Time

:

Milestone

Name

Signature

No.

Verified by

DIVE No.	DIVE LOG	Date

Dive Site   Boat/Shore/Inland

Buddies

Boat/Skipper   Port/Launch Site

Dive of Day   1   2   3   4 | Surface Int.   : | Time in   :   out   :

Mix	Pressure		Used	Cyl. Size	DIVE TIME	MAX DEPTH
	In	Out				
					mins	m/ft

Tissue Code: Pre   Post   Deco Stops......... mins .... m/ft ....mins........ m/ft

Equipment Notes	Weather/Sea Conditions	Training/Practice Needed

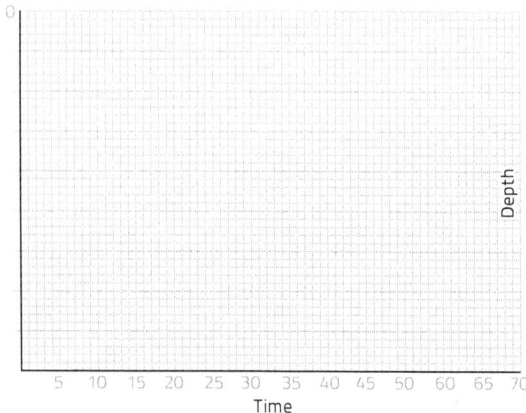

Depth / Time

Issues

Nitrogen Narcosis

Buddy Separation

Kit Failure

Working Hard

Unhappy

Missed Deco Stop

Other

Summary	Estimated Visibility
	_____ m/ft

Description/Sketch/Memory of Dive

Accumulated Dive Time	Name	**Verified by**
:	Signature	
Milestone	No.	

DIVE No.	DIVE LOG	Date

Dive Site   Boat/Shore/Inland

Buddies

Boat/Skipper   Port/Launch Site

Dive of Day 1 2 3 4   Surface Int.   :   Time in   :   out   :

Mix	Pressure		Used	Cyl. Size	DIVE TIME	MAX DEPTH
	In	Out				
					mins	m/ft

Tissue Code: Pre   Post   Deco Stops......... mins .... m/ft ....mins........ m/ft

Equipment Notes	Weather/Sea Conditions	Training/Practice Needed

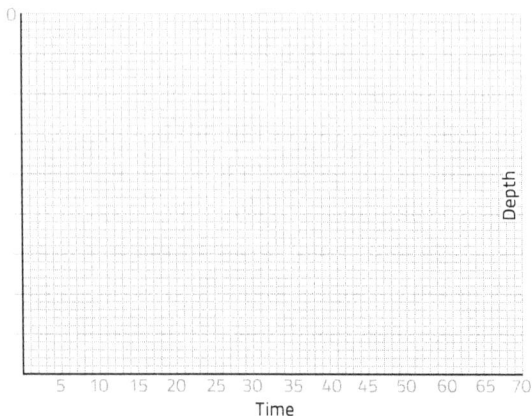

Issues

Nitrogen Narcosis

Buddy Separation

Kit Failure

Working Hard

Unhappy

Missed Deco Stop

Other

Depth

Time

5 10 15 20 25 30 35 40 45 50 60 65 70

Summary

Estimated Visibility

_____ m/ft

Description/Sketch/Memory of Dive

Accumulated Dive Time

:

Milestone

Name

Signature

No.

Verified by

DIVE No.	DIVE LOG	Date

Dive Site   Boat/Shore/Inland

Buddies

Boat/Skipper   Port/Launch Site

Dive of Day 1 2 3 4   Surface Int. :   Time in :   out :

Mix	Pressure		Used	Cyl. Size	DIVE TIME	MAX DEPTH
	In	Out				
					mins	m/ft

Tissue Code: Pre   Post   Deco Stops......... mins........ m/ft ....mins........ m/ft

Equipment Notes	Weather/Sea Conditions	Training/Practice Needed

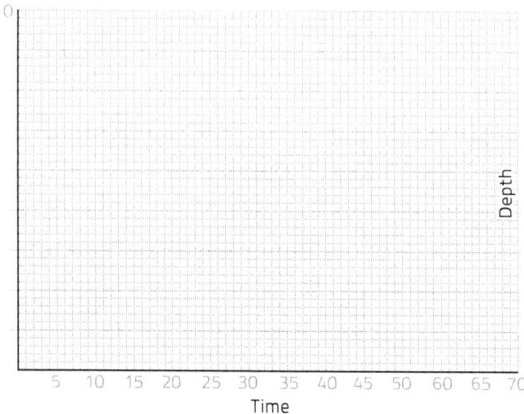

Issues

Nitrogen Narcosis

Buddy Separation

Kit Failure

Working Hard

Unhappy

Missed Deco Stop

Other

5   10   15   20   25   30   35   40   45   50   55   60   65   70

Time

Depth

Summary

Estimated Visibility

________________m/ft

Description/Sketch/Memory of Dive

Accumulated Dive Time

:

Milestone

Name

Signature

No.

Verified by

DIVE No.   DIVE LOG   **Date**

Dive Site   Boat/Shore/Inland

Buddies

Boat/Skipper   Port/Launch Site

Dive of Day 1 2 3 4   Surface Int.   :   Time in   :   out   :

Mix	Pressure		Used	Cyl. Size	DIVE TIME	MAX DEPTH
	In	Out				
					mins	m/ft

Tissue Code: Pre   Post   Deco Stops......... mins .... m/ft ....mins........ m/ft

Equipment Notes	Weather/Sea Conditions	Training/Practice Needed

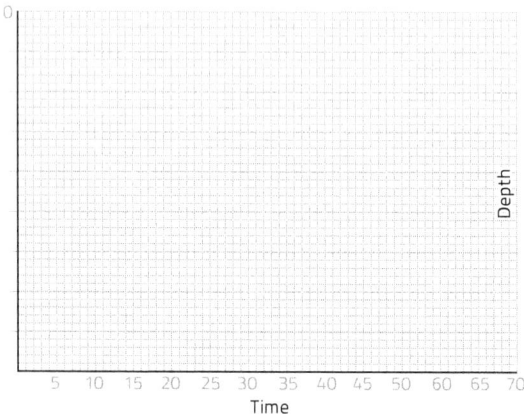

Issues

Nitrogen Narcosis

Buddy Separation

Kit Failure

Working Hard

Unhappy

Missed Deco Stop

Other

Depth

5 10 15 20 25 30 35 40 45 50 55 60 65 70

Time

Summary

Estimated Visibility

_____ m/ft

Description/Sketch/Memory of Dive

_____

_____

_____

_____

_____

_____

_____

_____

_____

_____

_____

_____

_____

_____

_____

_____

_____

_____

_____

_____

_____

_____

_____

Accumulated Dive Time	Name	**Verified by**
:	Signature	
Milestone	No.	

| DIVE No. | DIVE LOG | Date |

Dive Site Boat/Shore/Inland

Buddies

Boat/Skipper Port/Launch Site

Dive of Day 1 2 3 4   Surface Int.   :   Time in   :   out   :

Mix	Pressure In	Pressure Out	Used	Cyl. Size	DIVE TIME	MAX DEPTH
					mins	m/ft

Tissue Code: Pre   Post   Deco Stops......... mins .... m/ft ....mins........ m/ft

| Equipment Notes | Weather/Sea Conditions | Training/Practice Needed |

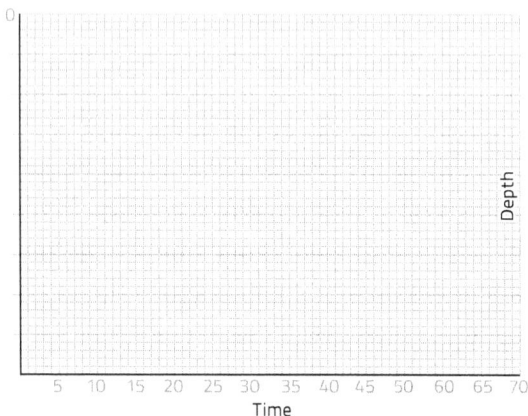

Depth / Time graph

5   10   15   20   25   30   35   40   45   50   60   65   70
Time

Issues

Nitrogen Narcosis

Buddy Separation

Kit Failure

Working Hard

Unhappy

Missed Deco Stop

Other

Summary

Description/Sketch/Memory of Dive

Accumulated Dive Time

:

Milestone

Name

Signature

No.

Verified by

| DIVE No. | DIVE LOG | Date |

Dive Site Boat/Shore/Inland

Buddies

Boat/Skipper   Port/Launch Site

Dive of Day 1 2 3 4   Surface Int.   :   Time in   :   out   :

	Pressure			Cyl.	**DIVE TIME**	**MAX DEPTH**
Mix	In	Out	Used	Size		
					mins	m/ft

Tissue Code: Pre   Post   Deco Stops......... mins .... m/ft ....mins........ m/ft

| Equipment Notes | Weather/Sea Conditions | Training/Practice Needed |

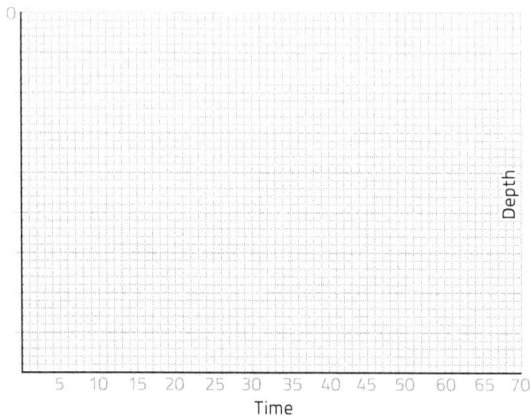

0

Depth

5   10   15   20   25   30   35   40   45   50   60   65   70

Time

Issues

Nitrogen Narcosis

Buddy Separation

Kit Failure

Working Hard

Unhappy

Missed Deco Stop

Other _____

Summary

Estimated Visibility

_____ m/ft

Description/Sketch/Memory of Dive

Accumulated Dive Time

:

Milestone

Name

Signature

No.

Verified by

DIVE No.	DIVE LOG	Date

Dive Site   Boat/Shore/Inland

Buddies

Boat/Skipper   Port/Launch Site

Dive of Day 1 2 3 4 | Surface Int. : | Time in : out :

Mix	Pressure		Used	Cyl. Size	DIVE TIME	MAX DEPTH
	In	Out				
					mins	m/ft

Tissue Code: Pre   Post   Deco Stops......... mins .... m/ft ....mins........ m/ft

Equipment Notes	Weather/Sea Conditions	Training/Practice Needed

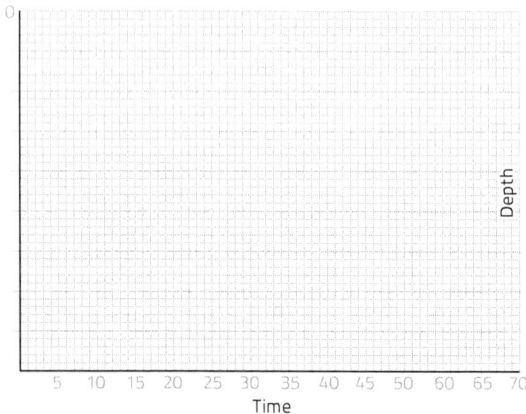

Issues

Nitrogen Narcosis

Buddy Separation

Kit Failure

Working Hard

Unhappy

Missed Deco Stop

Other _____

Depth

5   10   15   20   25   30   35   40   45   50   55   60   65   70
Time

Summary

Estimated Visibility

_____ m/ft

Description/Sketch/Memory of Dive

Accumulated Dive Time		
:	Name	**Verified by**
Milestone	Signature	
	No.	

DIVE No.	DIVE LOG	Date

Dive Site   Boat/Shore/Inland

Buddies

Boat/Skipper   Port/Launch Site

Dive of Day 1 2 3 4   Surface Int.   :   Time in   :   out   :

	Pressure			Cyl.		
Mix	In	Out	Used	Size	**DIVE TIME**	**MAX DEPTH**
					mins	m/ft

Tissue Code: Pre   Post   Deco Stops......... mins .... m/ft ....mins........ m/ft

Equipment Notes	Weather/Sea Conditions	Training/Practice Needed

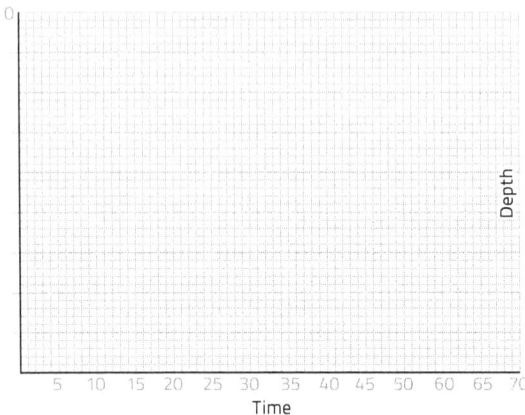

Issues

Nitrogen Narcosis

Buddy Separation

Kit Failure

Working Hard

Unhappy

Missed Deco Stop

Other

Depth

Time

5   10   15   20   25   30   35   40   45   50   60   65   70

Summary

Estimated Visibility

m/ft

Description/Sketch/Memory of Dive

Accumulated Dive Time

:

Milestone

Name

Signature

No.

Verified by

DIVE No.	DIVE LOG	Date

Dive Site Boat/Shore/Inland

Buddies

Boat/Skipper Port/Launch Site

Dive of Day 1 2 3 4 Surface Int.   : Time in   : out   :

Mix	Pressure In	Pressure Out	Used	Cyl. Size	DIVE TIME	MAX DEPTH
					mins	m/ft

Tissue Code: Pre   Post   Deco Stops......... mins .... m/ft ....mins........ m/ft

Equipment Notes	Weather/Sea Conditions	Training/Practice Needed

Time

Depth

Issues

Nitrogen Narcosis

Buddy Separation

Kit Failure

Working Hard

Unhappy

Missed Deco Stop

Other

Summary

Estimated Visibility

_____m/ft

Description/Sketch/Memory of Dive

Accumulated Dive Time

:

Milestone

Name

Signature

No.

Verified by

| DIVE No. | **DIVE LOG** | Date |

Dive Site
Boat/Shore/Inland

Buddies

Boat/Skipper   Port/Launch Site

Dive of Day 1 2 3 4 | Surface Int. : | Time in : out :

Mix	Pressure		Used	Cyl. Size	DIVE TIME	MAX DEPTH
	In	Out				
					mins	m/ft

Tissue Code: Pre   Post   Deco Stops......... mins .... m/ft ....mins........ m/ft

Equipment Notes	Weather/Sea Conditions	Training/Practice Needed

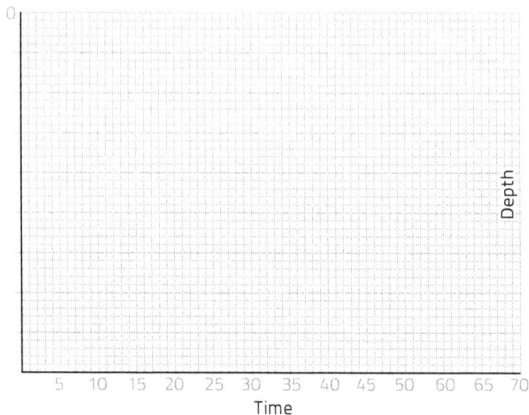

Time

Issues
Nitrogen Narcosis

Buddy Separation

Kit Failure

Working Hard

Unhappy

Missed Deco Stop

Other

Summary

Estimated Visibility

_____ m/ft

Description/Sketch/Memory of Dive

Accumulated Dive Time	Name	Verified by
:	Signature	
Milestone	No.	

DIVE No.	DIVE LOG	Date

Dive Site   Boat/Shore/Inland

Buddies

Boat/Skipper   Port/Launch Site

Dive of Day   1   2   3   4   Surface Int.   :   Time in   :   out   :

	Pressure			Cyl.	DIVE TIME	MAX DEPTH
Mix	In	Out	Used	Size		
					mins	m/ft

Tissue Code: Pre   Post   Deco Stops......... mins .... m/ft ....mins........ m/ft

Equipment Notes	Weather/Sea Conditions	Training/Practice Needed

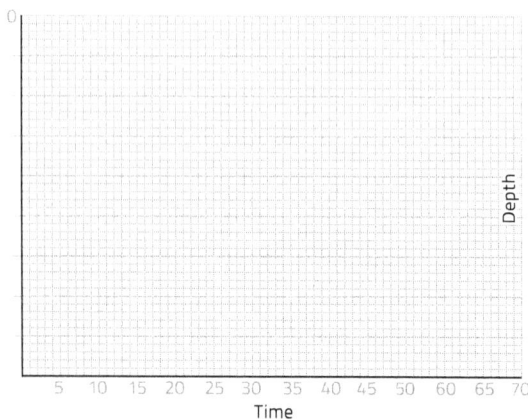

Issues

Nitrogen Narcosis

Buddy Separation

Kit Failure

Working Hard

Unhappy

Missed Deco Stop

Other

Summary

Estimated Visibility

_____ m/ft

Description/Sketch/Memory of Dive

Accumulated Dive Time

:

Milestone

Name

Signature

No.

Verified by

| DIVE No. | **DIVE LOG** | Date |

| Dive Site | Boat/Shore/Inland |

Buddies

Boat/Skipper   Port/Launch Site

Dive of Day   1 2 3 4   Surface Int.   :   Time in   :   out   :

| Mix | Pressure | | Used | Cyl. Size | DIVE TIME | MAX DEPTH |
	In	Out				
					mins	m/ft

Tissue Code: Pre   Post   Deco Stops......... mins .... m/ft ....mins........ m/ft

| Equipment Notes | Weather/Sea Conditions | Training/Practice Needed |

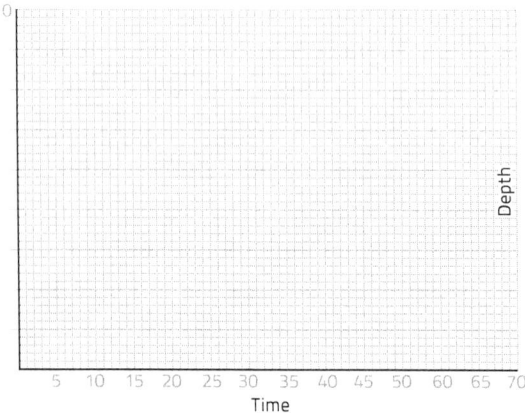

Depth / Time

Issues

Nitrogen Narcosis

Buddy Separation

Kit Failure

Working Hard

Unhappy

Missed Deco Stop

Other _____

Summary

Estimated Visibility

_____m/ft

Description/Sketch/Memory of Dive

Accumulated Dive Time	Name	**Verified by**
:	Signature	
Milestone	No.	

DIVE No.	DIVE LOG	Date

Dive Site	Boat/Shore/Inland

Buddies

Boat/Skipper   Port/Launch Site

Dive of Day 1 2 3 4   Surface Int.   :   Time in   :   out   :

	Pressure			Cyl.	**DIVE TIME**	**MAX DEPTH**
Mix	In	Out	Used	Size		
					mins	m/ft

Tissue Code: Pre   Post   Deco Stops......... mins .... m/ft ....mins........ m/ft

Equipment Notes	Weather/Sea Conditions	Training/Practice Needed

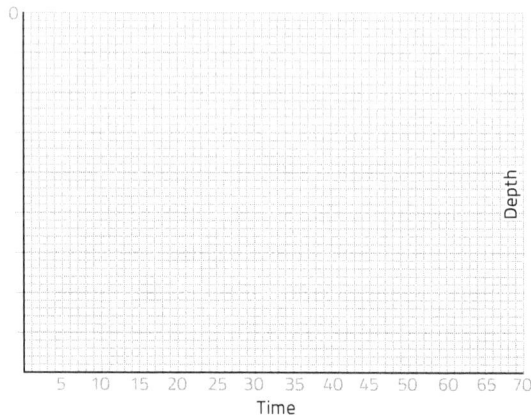

0

Depth

Time
5 10 15 20 25 30 35 40 45 50 55 60 65 70

Issues

Nitrogen Narcosis

Buddy Separation

Kit Failure

Working Hard

Unhappy

Missed Deco Stop

Other _____

Summary

Estimated Visibility

______ m/ft

Description/Sketch/Memory of Dive

Accumulated Dive Time

:

Milestone

Name

Signature

No.

Verified by

| DIVE No. | DIVE LOG | Date |

Dive Site   Boat/Shore/Inland

Buddies

Boat/Skipper   Port/Launch Site

Dive of Day   1   2   3   4   Surface Int.   :   Time in   :   out   :

	Pressure			Cyl.	DIVE TIME	MAX DEPTH
Mix	In	Out	Used	Size		
					mins	m/ft

Tissue Code: Pre   Post   Deco Stops......... mins .... m/ft ....mins........ m/ft

Equipment Notes	Weather/Sea Conditions	Training/Practice Needed

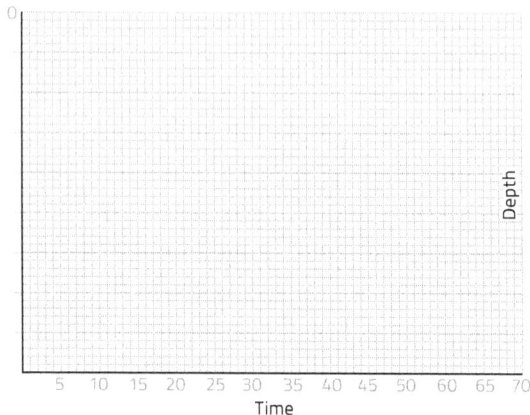

Issues

Nitrogen Narcosis

Buddy Separation

Kit Failure

Working Hard

Unhappy

Missed Deco Stop

Other

Depth

5   10   15   20   25   30   35   40   45   50   60   65   70

Time

Summary

Description/Sketch/Memory of Dive

Accumulated Dive Time		
:	Name	**Verified by**
Milestone	Signature	
	No.	

| DIVE No. | DIVE LOG | Date |

Dive Site   Boat/Shore/Inland

Buddies

Boat/Skipper   Port/Launch Site

Dive of Day 1 2 3 4   Surface Int.   :   Time in   :   out   :

Mix	Pressure		Used	Cyl. Size	DIVE TIME	MAX DEPTH
	In	Out				
					mins	m/ft

Tissue Code: Pre   Post   Deco Stops......... mins........ m/ft ....mins........ m/ft

| Equipment Notes | Weather/Sea Conditions | Training/Practice Needed |

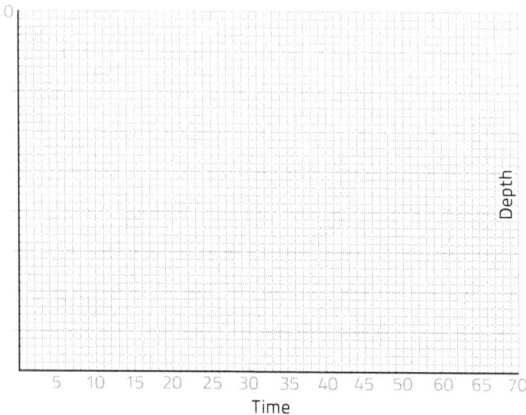

0

Depth

Time
5 10 15 20 25 30 35 40 45 50 60 65 70

Issues

Nitrogen Narcosis

Buddy Separation

Kit Failure

Working Hard

Unhappy

Missed Deco Stop

Other _____

Summary

Summary

Estimated Visibility

_____m/ft

Description/Sketch/Memory of Dive

Accumulated Dive Time

:

Milestone

Name

Signature

No.

Verified by

DIVE No.	DIVE LOG	Date

Dive Site Boat/Shore/Inland

Buddies

Boat/Skipper Port/Launch Site

Dive of Day 1 2 3 4 | Surface Int. : | Time in : out :

Mix	Pressure In	Pressure Out	Used	Cyl. Size	DIVE TIME	MAX DEPTH
					mins	m/ft

Tissue Code: Pre   Post   Deco Stops......... mins .... m/ft ....mins........ m/ft

Equipment Notes	Weather/Sea Conditions	Training/Practice Needed

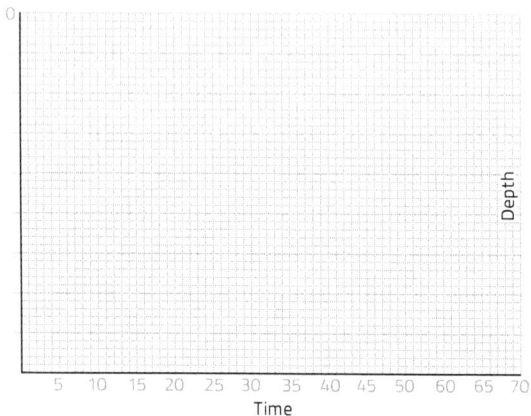

Issues

Nitrogen Narcosis

Buddy Separation

Kit Failure

Working Hard

Unhappy

Missed Deco Stop

Other

Depth

5 10 15 20 25 30 35 40 45 50 55 60 65 70

Time

Summary

Description/Sketch/Memory of Dive

Accumulated Dive Time	Name	Verified by
:	Signature	
Milestone	No.	

DIVE No.	DIVE LOG	Date

Dive Site   Boat/Shore/Inland

Buddies

Boat/Skipper   Port/Launch Site

Dive of Day   1   2   3   4   Surface Int.   :   Time in   :   out   :

	Pressure			Cyl.	**DIVE TIME**	**MAX DEPTH**
Mix	In	Out	Used	Size		
					mins	m/ft

Tissue Code: Pre   Post   Deco Stops......... mins .... m/ft ....mins........ m/ft

Equipment Notes	Weather/Sea Conditions	Training/Practice Needed

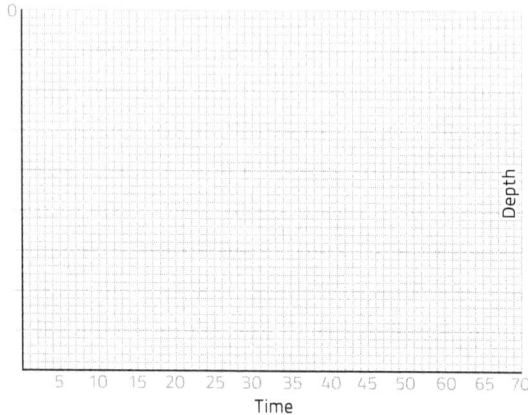

Issues

Nitrogen Narcosis

Buddy Separation

Kit Failure

Working Hard

Unhappy

Missed Deco Stop

Other

0

Depth

5   10   15   20   25   30   35   40   45   50   60   65   70

Time

Summary

Estimated Visibility

______ m/ft

Description/Sketch/Memory of Dive

Accumulated Dive Time

:

Milestone

Name

Signature

No.

Verified by

| DIVE No. | DIVE LOG | Date |

| Dive Site | | Boat/Shore/Inland |

Buddies

Boat/Skipper   Port/Launch Site

Dive of Day 1 2 3 4 | Surface Int. : | Time in : out :

Mix	Pressure		Used	Cyl. Size	DIVE TIME	MAX DEPTH
	In	Out				
					mins	m/ft

Tissue Code: Pre   Post | Deco Stops......... mins .... m/ft ....mins........ m/ft

| Equipment Notes | Weather/Sea Conditions | Training/Practice Needed |

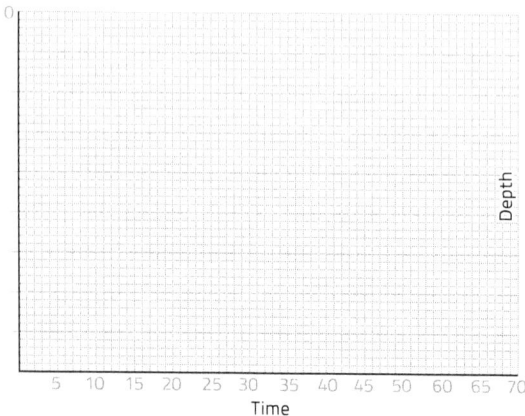

Time

Depth

Issues

Nitrogen Narcosis

Buddy Separation

Kit Failure

Working Hard

Unhappy

Missed Deco Stop

Other

Summary

Estimated Visibility
_____m/ft

Description/Sketch/Memory of Dive

Accumulated Dive Time

:

Milestone

Name

Signature

No.

Verified by

DIVE No.	DIVE LOG	Date

Dive Site Boat/Shore/Inland

Buddies

Boat/Skipper Port/Launch Site

Dive of Day 1 2 3 4   Surface Int. :   Time in :   out :

Mix	Pressure		Used	Cyl. Size	DIVE TIME	MAX DEPTH
	In	Out				
					mins	m/ft

Tissue Code: Pre   Post   Deco Stops......... mins........ m/ft ....mins........ m/ft

Equipment Notes	Weather/Sea Conditions	Training/Practice Needed

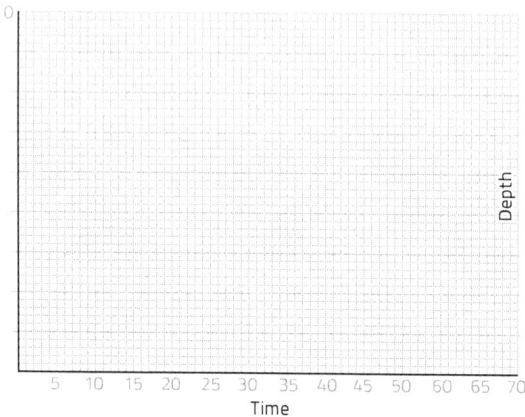

0

Depth

5 10 15 20 25 30 35 40 45 50 55 60 65 70
Time

Issues

Nitrogen Narcosis

Buddy Separation

Kit Failure

Working Hard

Unhappy

Missed Deco Stop

Other

Summary

Estimated Visibility

_____ m/ft

Description/Sketch/Memory of Dive

Accumulated Dive Time

:

Milestone

Name

Signature

No.

Verified by

DIVE No.	DIVE LOG	Date

Dive Site   Boat/Shore/Inland

Buddies

Boat/Skipper   Port/Launch Site

Dive of Day 1 2 3 4   Surface Int.   :   Time in   :   out   :

	Pressure			Cyl.	**DIVE TIME**	**MAX DEPTH**
Mix	In	Out	Used	Size		
					mins	m/ft

Tissue Code: Pre   Post   Deco Stops......... mins .... m/ft ....mins........ m/ft

Equipment Notes	Weather/Sea Conditions	Training/Practice Needed

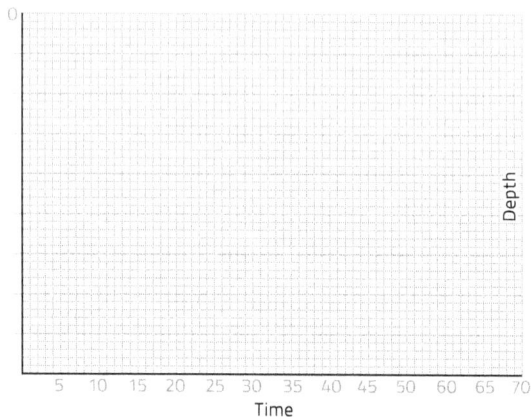

Issues

Nitrogen Narcosis

Buddy Separation

Kit Failure

Working Hard

Unhappy

Missed Deco Stop

Other

5   10   15   20   25   30   35   40   45   50   60   65   70

Time

Depth

Summary

Description/Sketch/Memory of Dive

Accumulated Dive Time

:

Milestone

Name

Signature

No.

Verified by

DIVE No.	DIVE LOG	Date

Dive Site   Boat/Shore/Inland

Buddies

Boat/Skipper   Port/Launch Site

Dive of Day 1 2 3 4 | Surface Int. : | Time in : out :

Mix	Pressure		Used	Cyl. Size	DIVE TIME	MAX DEPTH
	In	Out				
					mins	m/ft

Tissue Code: Pre   Post   Deco Stops......... mins........ m/ft ....mins........ m/ft

Equipment Notes	Weather/Sea Conditions	Training/Practice Needed

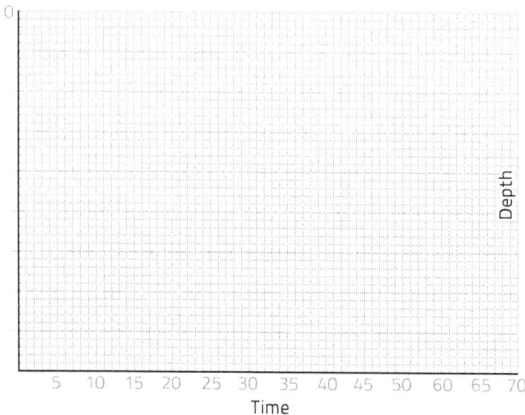

Depth / Time

Issues

Nitrogen Narcosis

Buddy Separation

Kit Failure

Working Hard

Unhappy

Missed Deco Stop

Other

Summary

Estimated Visibility

_____m/ft

Description/Sketch/Memory of Dive

Accumulated Dive Time

:

Milestone

Name

Signature

No.

Verified by

DIVE No.	DIVE LOG	Date

Dive Site Boat/Shore/Inland

Buddies

Boat/Skipper Port/Launch Site

Dive of Day 1 2 3 4   Surface Int. :   Time in :   out :

Mix	Pressure In	Pressure Out	Used	Cyl. Size	DIVE TIME	MAX DEPTH
					mins	m/ft

Tissue Code: Pre   Post   Deco Stops......... mins........ m/ft ....mins........ m/ft

Equipment Notes	Weather/Sea Conditions	Training/Practice Needed

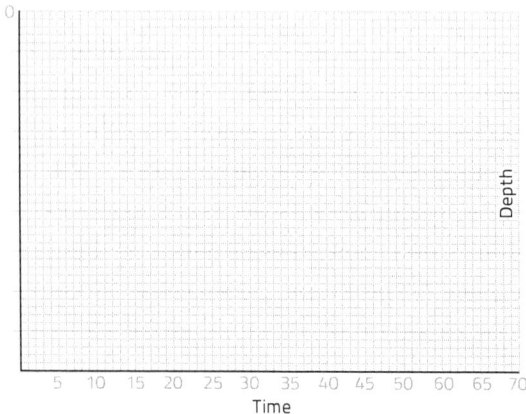

0

Depth

Time

5   10   15   20   25   30   35   40   45   50   55   60   65   70

Issues

Nitrogen Narcosis

Buddy Separation

Kit Failure

Working Hard

Unhappy

Missed Deco Stop

Other

Summary

Estimated Visibility

_____ m/ft

Description/Sketch/Memory of Dive

Accumulated Dive Time

:

Milestone

Name

Signature

No.

Verified by

DIVE No.	DIVE LOG	Date

Dive Site   Boat/Shore/Inland

Buddies

Boat/Skipper   Port/Launch Site

Dive of Day   1   2   3   4   Surface Int.   :   Time in   :   out   :

	Pressure			Cyl.	DIVE TIME	MAX DEPTH
Mix	In	Out	Used	Size		
					mins	m/ft

Tissue Code: Pre   Post   Deco Stops......... mins .... m/ft ....mins........ m/ft

Equipment Notes	Weather/Sea Conditions	Training/Practice Needed

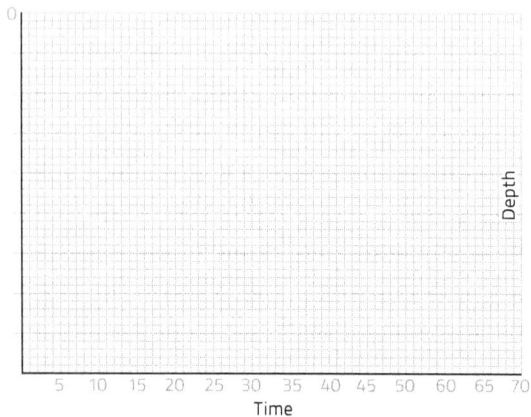

Issues

Nitrogen Narcosis

Buddy Separation

Kit Failure

Working Hard

Unhappy

Missed Deco Stop

Other

Depth

5   10   15   20   25   30   35   40   45   50   60   65   70

Time

Summary

Estimated Visibility

______ m/ft

Description/Sketch/Memory of Dive

Accumulated Dive Time

:

Milestone

Name

Signature

No.

Verified by

DIVE No.	DIVE LOG	Date

Dive Site	Boat/Shore/Inland

Buddies

Boat/Skipper	Port/Launch Site

Dive of Day 1 2 3 4   Surface Int.   :   Time in   :   out   :

Mix	Pressure		Used	Cyl. Size	DIVE TIME	MAX DEPTH
	In	Out				
					mins	m/ft

Tissue Code: Pre   Post   Deco Stops......... mins........ m/ft ....mins........ m/ft

Equipment Notes	Weather/Sea Conditions	Training/Practice Needed

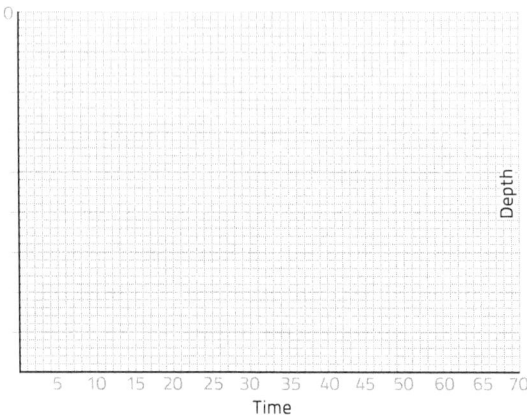

Time

Depth

Issues

Nitrogen Narcosis

Buddy Separation

Kit Failure

Working Hard

Unhappy

Missed Deco Stop

Other

Summary

Estimated Visibility

_____ m/ft

Description/Sketch/Memory of Dive

Accumulated Dive Time

:

Milestone

Name

Signature

No.

Verified by

DIVE No.	DIVE LOG	Date

Dive Site · Boat/Shore/Inland

Buddies

Boat/Skipper · Port/Launch Site

Dive of Day 1 2 3 4 · Surface Int.   : · Time in   :   out   :

Mix	Pressure		Used	Cyl. Size	DIVE TIME	MAX DEPTH
	In	Out				
					mins	m/ft

Tissue Code: Pre   Post · Deco Stops......... mins .... m/ft ....mins........ m/ft

Equipment Notes	Weather/Sea Conditions	Training/Practice Needed

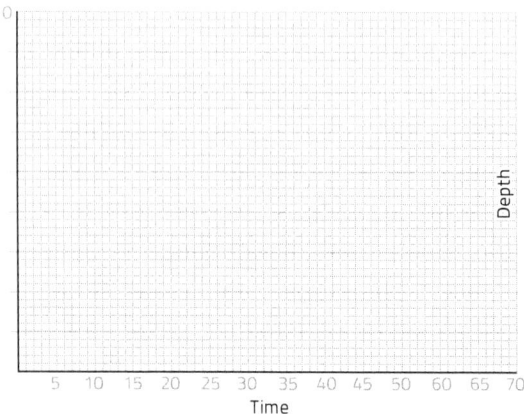

Issues

Nitrogen Narcosis

Buddy Separation

Kit Failure

Working Hard

Unhappy

Missed Deco Stop

Other

Depth

5   10   15   20   25   30   35   40   45   50   55   60   65   70

Time

Summary

Summary

Estimated Visibility

_____ m/ft

Description/Sketch/Memory of Dive

Accumulated Dive Time

:

Milestone

Name

Signature

No.

Verified by